little convent in the BIG CITY

The Unsolvable Problem

Mother Clare, CFR

ILLUSTRATIONS BY

Michael Corsini

VIANNEY VOCATIONS

Illustrated by Michael Corsini
www.michaelcorsini.com

Vianney Vocations
Tallahassee, Florida
www.vianneyvocations.com

for
Evelyn Chiara

FLOWERS

Once upon a time there was a little convent in a big city.

Now when I say big, I mean really big. In fact, it is the biggest city in our whole country. Have you guessed the city yet?

Home of the Empire State Building, home of the Statue of Liberty, home of Yankee Stadium, home of St. Patrick's Cathedral, home to over 8 million people, including Sr. Mary Andy and her Sisters.

It's New York City.

That brings me to the little convent. Little as in: small, petite, quaint. Convent as in: a house for Sisters.

A convent is a house like houses you have in your neighborhood, but it is a very special one. It has most of the things other houses have like windows and doors, sinks and refrigerators, tables and chairs, but one thing convents have that regular houses do not have is a chapel. A chapel is like a miniature church. The chapel is there so that Jesus can live in the convent with the Sisters, and the Sisters with Jesus.

That's what makes a convent a convent and not just a regular house: Jesus and Sisters

Sr. Mary Andy loves the chapel. She loves the kitchen too and the library and even the mail room has a special place in her heart, but nothing comes close to the chapel. All the Sisters gather there to pray five times a day.

When the bell rings, all the Sisters stop whatever they are doing and come to the chapel. It's like when your mom calls you from the kitchen window when you are playing in the backyard, or from the bench, when you are playing in the park. Whether you are sliding or swinging, tossing or talking, you stop what you are doing, because when your mother calls, you come.

The Sisters obey the voice of the bell like you obey the voice of your mother (or at least the way you *should* obey the voice of your mother): promptly, immediately, without hesitation.

Now back to Sr. Mary Andy. I was telling you how much she loves the chapel. It's quiet and peaceful in the chapel and Jesus is there always waiting for a visit. Jesus in the Blessed Sacrament waits patiently for the Sisters to come and spend a little time with Him. Sr. Mary Andy loves to come to the chapel five times a day when the bell rings and all the Sisters gather to pray together. And she also likes to come in between times too, when she can spend a few minutes in the chapel praying to Jesus all by herself.

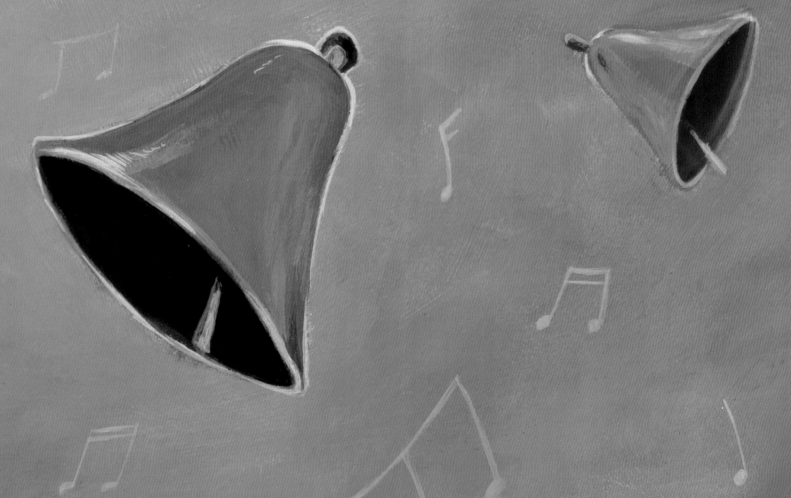

Have you ever been in a church all alone? Probably not at your age; you are always with your mother or father or sister or brother or aunt or uncle or teacher or someone. But I bet there is a quiet place in your house where you can go sometimes for a quiet moment of prayer. Maybe even in your own bedroom. Just go inside, shut the door, and say a quiet prayer to Jesus in secret. Try it!

Now, before we go any further, I have to be sure we are on the same page (that means that we understand each other). When I say Jesus is in the chapel, I mean Jesus in the Blessed Sacrament—in the Host, just like at Mass on Sunday. If sometimes I say "God" and sometimes I say "Jesus," it's not because I got sleepy while writing this. No! It's because the Host is Jesus and Jesus is God.

You probably knew that already, but just in case you didn't, I did not want you to be confused.

Now, back to Sr. Mary Andy. When Sr. Mary Andy stops in to make a visit to Jesus in the tabernacle sometimes it's to say thank you. Today Sr. Mary Andy found out that a man she'd been praying for found a job. She wanted to jump and shout and do a cartwheel because she was so excited, but instead she ran to the chapel to say thanks to God. Then she came out of the chapel and did a cartwheel.

Do you have anything you want to thank God for? You can thank Him right now before you turn the page.

One day Sr. Mary Andy was on her way to the chapel. Very often, when Sister has a problem, she goes to the chapel to ask for God's help to solve it. Today Sr. Mary Andy had a big problem, a huge problem, an unsolvable problem.

Have you ever had a big problem, a huge problem, an unsolvable problem? What about a small problem? Who do you go to for help? Your mother? Your father?

You can also tell your problems to God. He is always listening.

Now back to Sr. Mary Andy. Her big problem, her huge problem, her unsolvable problem was this: it was the third of July.

Now that may not sound like a problem, but keep reading. It was! The third of July is very close to the Fourth of July, and the Fourth of July is a great day, a wonderful day, a day to celebrate the birthday of America—Independence Day! The Fourth of July means hamburgers and hot dogs, root beer floats, fireworks and sparklers, and the Stars and Stripes flying high.

Do you celebrate the Fourth of July? Sr. Mary Andy loved to celebrate it with her family when she was little like you. She especially loved root beer floats and fireworks.

Have you ever had a root beer float? Take a tall glass, put in two scoops of vanilla ice cream, then pour in the root beer over the ice cream. (Pour slowly because it will foam up and overflow if you pour too quickly.) If you don't care for root beer you can use coke or orange soda. Then put in a straw and a spoon because you'll need both. Enjoy!

Now, before we get back to Sr. Mary Andy and her big problem, her huge problem, her unsolvable problem, you have to know a little bit more information about Sr. Mary Andy and her Sisters and their life in the big city. Besides spending a lot of time in the chapel, they also spend a lot of time out of the chapel, out in the city.

You see, the Sisters spend time out and about doing good deeds.

You may be wondering: "But what, exactly do they do? Are they teachers or surgeons, librarians or lawyers?"

The answer is yes, and it is also no. There are Sisters in the world who do all of those things. Some are teachers. Others are doctors and there are even Sisters who are lawyers. But Sr. Mary Andy and her Sisters are none of those things. Rather, they are like mothers—not mothers to children or babies, but mothers to the poor.

They are busy seeing and noticing and helping people that sometimes go unseen, unnoticed, and unhelped. Have you ever seen a poor person sitting on the sidewalk? Did you wonder why he was sitting there? In a big city like New York there are many people who for one reason or another do not have what you and I have. They do not even have the basic things that everybody needs.

Sr. Mary Andy and the Sisters help these poor people.

One way the Sisters help those in need is by cooking hot meals and then inviting anyone who is hungry over to the convent for lunch.

Now back to Sr. Mary Andy and her big problem, her huge problem, her unsolvable problem.

The Fourth of July was almost here, and Sr. Mary Andy wanted the hot meal for the poor people to be delicious, wonderful and perfect for the Fourth of July. She thought everyone would love to have a juicy hamburger and a root beer float.

Sr. Mary Andy made a list of all the things she needed and sure enough, Sr. Lily-May and Sr. Angelina found every last item on the list, except hamburger buns. There were no buns to be found. No buns in the breadbox, no buns in the fridge, no buns in the freezer, not even in the extra freezer down in the basement. There were no hamburger buns in the convent—not a bun, not a one.

This was Sr. Mary Andy's big problem, her huge problem, her unsolvable problem. How could they serve hamburgers with no buns? What would hold the ketchup, pickles, mayo, lettuce and onions? Bagels? Sliced bread? Croutons? French baguettes? Tortillas? No, no, those just wouldn't work.

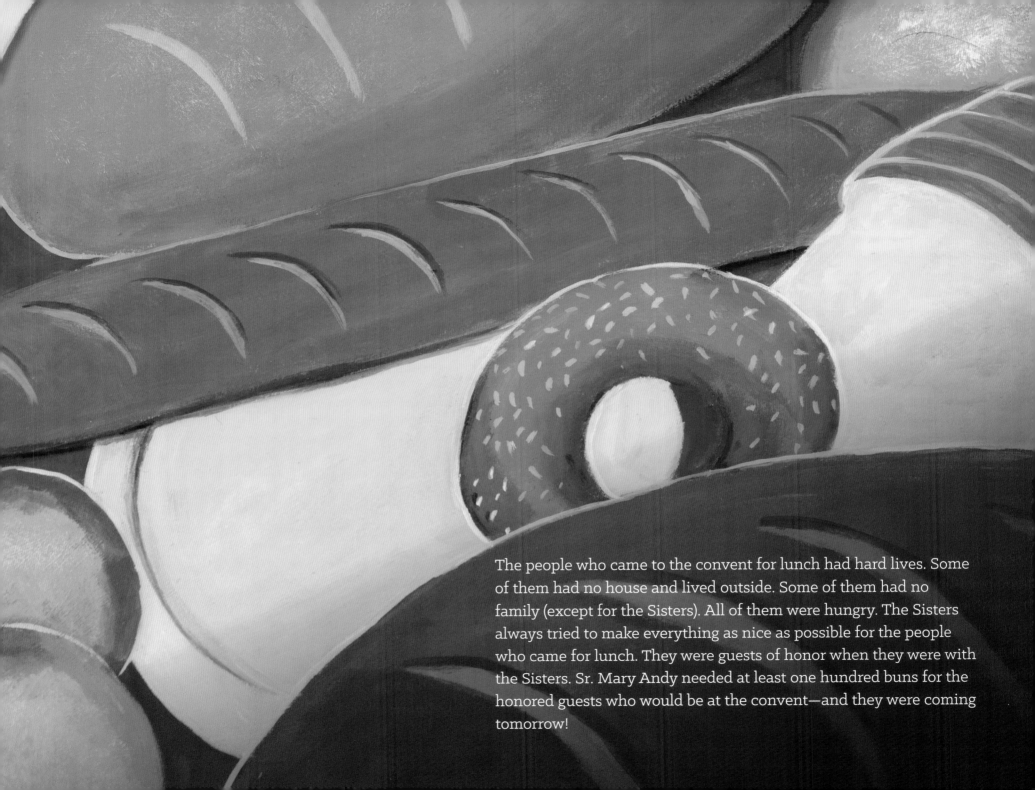

The people who came to the convent for lunch had hard lives. Some of them had no house and lived outside. Some of them had no family (except for the Sisters). All of them were hungry. The Sisters always tried to make everything as nice as possible for the people who came for lunch. They were guests of honor when they were with the Sisters. Sr. Mary Andy needed at least one hundred buns for the honored guests who would be at the convent—and they were coming tomorrow!

So, I bet you can guess where Sr. Mary Andy went with her big problem, her huge problem, her unsolvable problem. Did you guess the chapel? You are right!

Sr. Mary Andy made a visit to the chapel to explain her problem to Jesus and to ask for His help. No sooner had she gotten out her problem and finished her prayer when Sr. Angelina came to find her, because there was a lot to do to get ready for a hundred honored guests.

There was cooking and cleaning and table setting to do. There were decorations to hang, flags to fly, and songs to practice.

All of the Sisters were busy. They counted forks and knives, plates and napkins. Floors were swept and mopped and the bathrooms were cleaned. Finally, the convent was ready and the American flag—Old Glory—was hung majestically from the second-story window. The only thing left to do was brush up on the patriotic hymns.

Just as the Sisters perfected the "Star Spangled Banner" and were on to "God Bless America," the doorbell rang. Now, you should know that when the doorbell rings in the convent, all the Sisters do not go running to answer the door all at once (like my brothers and sisters and I did when we were growing up). The Sisters take turns answering the door, and when it's your turn you are called the "portress" for the day.

Sr. Mary Andy was the portress on July third, and she went sailing out of the music practice to the words "land that I love…"

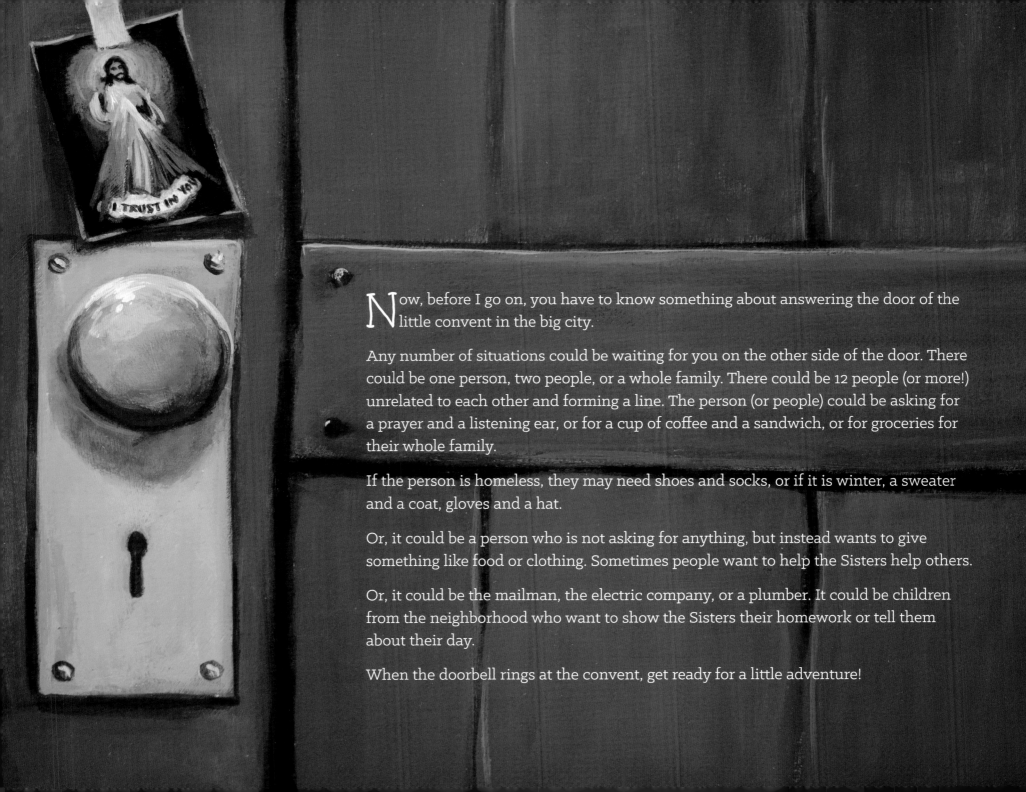

Now, before I go on, you have to know something about answering the door of the little convent in the big city.

Any number of situations could be waiting for you on the other side of the door. There could be one person, two people, or a whole family. There could be 12 people (or more!) unrelated to each other and forming a line. The person (or people) could be asking for a prayer and a listening ear, or for a cup of coffee and a sandwich, or for groceries for their whole family.

If the person is homeless, they may need shoes and socks, or if it is winter, a sweater and a coat, gloves and a hat.

Or, it could be a person who is not asking for anything, but instead wants to give something like food or clothing. Sometimes people want to help the Sisters help others.

Or, it could be the mailman, the electric company, or a plumber. It could be children from the neighborhood who want to show the Sisters their homework or tell them about their day.

When the doorbell rings at the convent, get ready for a little adventure!

Now back to Sr. Mary Andy. The two men on the other side of the convent door were not asking for a cup of coffee or a sandwich or a bag of food. They came to make a donation. A donation is a gift. The donation was in two black garbage bags. Each man had one. "Do you need bread, Sister?" "We sure do!" said Sr. Mary Andy. "We can always use bread."

The two men handed the hefty bags to Sr. Mary Andy and turned to leave. "Thank you and God bless you," Sr. Mary Andy said as she closed the door behind them. Opening one of the bags and peaking inside, Sr. Mary Andy saw that the bread these men brought was not sliced bread, not French bread, not Italian bread, not scones, not bagels, not muffins—can you guess what kind of bread it was?

It was hamburger buns!

Two bags stuffed full of hamburger buns! Sr. Mary Andy let out a gasp and a "thank you Jesus, Mary, and Joseph" with her eyes raised to heaven.

Then she quickly opened the door to see if she could thank the men again and tell them that this was an answer to her prayers, but when she opened the door, they were already gone.

Sr. Mary Andy raced back to join the music practice in the library. When "Mine Eyes Have Seen the Glory" came to an end, she couldn't wait another minute to tell the Sisters about their mysterious delivery of hamburger buns.

The other Sisters were astonished. "Only hamburger buns? No other bread? Not sliced bread, not French bread, not Italian bread?"

"No other bread," said Sr. Mary Andy.

"No white bread, wheat bread, bagels, tortillas, or muffins? This has never happened before," said Sr. Lily-May. "I guess we didn't need it before," said Sr. Angelina.

At their night prayers, all the Sisters in the little convent in the big city thanked God for the gift of the hamburger buns.

The next morning Sr. Mary Andy woke up early, excited for the Fourth of July. The sky was blue, the sun was shining and everyone was in good spirits.

First, the volunteers arrived. There is a whole team of people who like to volunteer with the Sisters—helping them help the poor.

Once everything was set up and the food was ready, Sr. Mary Andy opened the front door and let in all the people who were waiting patiently outside to come in for lunch.

The first man to come in said, "Happy Fourth, Sister! I sure do hope we're having burgers today. I can't even remember the last time I had one!"

"We sure are! Hamburgers, root beer floats, and the Star-Spangled Banner," said Sr. Mary Andy.

Sr. Mary Andy's big problem, her huge problem, her unsolvable problem—was *solved*. And so, the little convent in the big city celebrated the Fourth of July with one hundred happy guests of honor because no problem is unsolvable with God.

The End.

little convent
in the
BIG CITY

The Franciscan Sisters of the Renewal were founded in the South Bronx to live and serve among the very poor. Ever since they began in 1988, God has shown His providential care for the Sisters and those they serve. This is one true story of God's amazing providence. There are so many more!